This book is dedicated to Aunt Gladys, who has a soft spot in her heart for all dogs.

Edited by Aileen Andres Sox
Designed by Dennis Ferree
Art by Mary Rumford
Typeset in 14/18 Weiss

ISBN: 0-8163-1095-5

92 93 94 95 96 • 5 4 3 2 1

Max
Moves
In

By Linda Porter Carlyle   Illustrated by Mary Rumford

Pacific Press Publishing Association
Boise, Idaho
Oshawa, Ontario, Canada

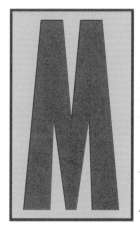ama wanted a puppy for her birthday. Papa bought her one for a surprise. "His name is Max," said Papa proudly.

Mama looked at Max. "Is this a *puppy?*" she asked.

"Of course," said Papa. "He's only six months old."

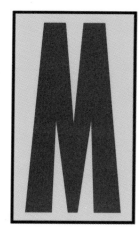ama looked at Max. "Will he get much bigger?" she asked.

"A little," said Papa cautiously.

Mama looked at Max. I laughed. Max was already as big as I am.

"Happy birthday, dear," said Papa.

Mama and I take Max for a walk every morning. He has a bright blue leash that fastens onto his collar. Max loves to walk.

Max pulls Mama down the sidewalk. He stops and sniffs bushes and flowers and invisible spots on the grass.

ood morning," Mr. Wilson calls to us over his fence. "Are you taking your dog for a walk, or is he taking you?" Mr. Wilson chuckles and cuts a rose for Mama.

 will take Max to obedience school," says Papa.

Max stands on the back porch with his front feet on the dining-room window. He puts his nose against the glass. He looks at me and barks. Max wants to come inside and play.

"Obedience school is a good idea," says Mama. "Max will be more fun to be around when he has learned to obey. He will be safer and happier."

You must be patient with your dog," the teacher says. "Some dogs learn very quickly. And some dogs need lots and lots of practice." The teacher looks at Papa and Max. Max bounces up and down at the end of his leash. He looks like a giant, fluffy white wind-up toy.

ou know," says Papa at suppertime, "we are all like Max."

I look at Papa with surprised eyes.

"The first thing Max had to learn at obedience school was to pay attention to me," Papa says. "He has to pay attention so he can know what I want him to do. We need to pay attention to Jesus. We need to know what He wants us to do."

apa and Max practice every day. Max is learning to walk beside Papa and not pull him down the street.

But Max doesn't walk perfectly with Papa yet. Sometimes he makes mistakes, and sometimes he is naughty. Sometimes he just sits there on the sidewalk panting, with his big tongue hanging out of his mouth.

"Come on, Max," Papa coaxes.

ometimes Max sees something he would like to chase, like leaves or Mrs. Scriven's cat. "Come back, Max!" Papa shouts.

apa is patient. He keeps working with Max. Papa smiles and says, "Well, Max, old boy, I love you. We'll try it again tomorrow."

I think God is like Papa. God is patient with me. Sometimes I make mistakes, and sometimes I am naughty. God smiles at me and says, "Well, little girl, I love you. We'll try it again tomorrow."

od, please help me obey Your rules, because that makes me happy.
Help me want to obey Your rules, because that makes You glad.

Parent's Guide

Ways to Teach Obedience With Patience

Love, trust, and obedience are the most important early spiritual lessons your child needs to learn. They can be learned only one way—through experiencing a loving, trusting relationship with his or her parents. Here are some ways to implement the ideas about obedience and patience in *Max Moves In*:

❖ Overwhelm your child with messages of love and approval. Seventy-five to 90 percent of the messages he hears from your lips should be positive. Your child (and your spouse and you) will thrive in such a positive environment.

❖ Remember that saying No can be another way of saying, "I love you." Set boundaries and enforce them kindly, confidently, and consistently.

❖ Follow correction with a hug or kiss. Never deny your child the comfort of your love just because she has disobeyed.

❖ Be sure your child knows that you are labeling only his behavior bad; *he* is your beloved child.

❖ God often lets His willful children learn the hard way—by suffering the consequences of their sins and mistakes. Discipline that allows a child to see the consequences of his actions is more effective than physical punishment.

❖ Try to distinguish between willful disobedience and childish irresponsibility or misbehavior because of factors such as fatigue.

Willful disobedience calls for punishment that fits the disobedience. Irresponsibility or other types of misbehavior call for patient teaching and reminding.

❖ When parental fatigue and impatience meet childish behavior or misbehavior, a wise parent will remove him- or herself or the child from the scene rather than act impatiently. Do nothing until you can act calmly. When you react badly, ask your child's forgiveness.

❖ A home that runs on schedule with meals and bedtimes adhered to closely is a home where parents can be more patient and children more obedient because physical needs are met.

❖ When you think about bringing patience and obedience together in your family, hold this picture of God in your mind: "The Lord is not slow in doing what he promised—the way some people understand slowness. But God is being patient with you. He does not want anyone to be lost. He wants everyone to change his heart and life" (2 Peter 3:9, International Children's Bible).

Linda Porter Carlyle and Aileen Andres Sox

Books by Linda Porter Carlyle

I Can Choose
A Child's Steps to Jesus
God and Joseph and Me
Rescued From the River!
Grandma Stepped on Fred!
Max Moves In